The Voter
by Chinua Achebe

Published by ViVa Books
PO Box 28510, Kensington 2101, South Africa

First published 1994
Reprinted 1995 (twice)
Reprinted 1996
Reprinted 1999
Reprinted 2004

Cover illustration by Renée Koch

Acknowledgements
Photograph of Chinua Achebe with permission from Heinemann-Centaur Publishers. Illustrations on pages 38, 39, 43 courtesy of IDASA.

ISBN 1 874932 13 1

Reproduction by Remata Bureau and Printers, Midrand

Printed and bound Jakaranda Printers, Rosslyn

Some facts about the writer

Chinua Achebe was born in 1930 in the village of Ogidi in Eastern Nigeria. He was educated at Government College, Umuahia and the University of Ibadan in Nigeria. He studied medicine and literature.

His first book was published in 1958. It is called *Things Fall Apart*. This is his most famous book. It has sold over three million copies in 30 different languages. He has another famous book called *A Man of the People*. This is about Nigeria after independence. He has also written children's books. Achebe also worked as an editor for Heinemann Educational Books on their African Writers Series of books. His own writing and his work as an editor have had a great influence on African writing.

Achebe also worked for the Nigerian Broadcasting Corporation and later at universities in America. He has received many awards. In 1987 he received the Nigerian National Merit award. This is Nigeria's highest award for intellectual achievement.

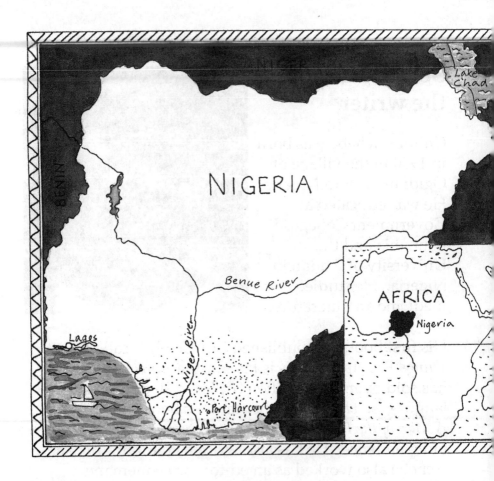

Introduction

This story takes place in a village in Nigeria. Look at the map of Africa to find Nigeria. The story tells us about the difficult decisions people face when voting in an election. The book also teaches us about elections and voting in South Africa.

Roof and the Honourable Minister

Rufus Okeke lived in the village of Umuofia.
Rufus, who was called 'Roof' for short, was a
very popular man. The villagers did not say so
straight out, but they were thankful that Roof
stayed in Umuofia. These days most young men
left the village to look for work in the towns.

Tower Hamlets	
Suppliers Code	AVA
Price	£4.50
Invoice Date	01/11/2006
LOC	BOW
Class	428.6
Barcode	C001279313

Roof was not a lazy man either. For two years he had worked in Port Harcourt. He was learning to fix bicycles. Then he gave up a bright future there and returned to the village. There was an election coming. Roof wanted to guide his people in these hard times.

Umuofia did not really need to be guided. The whole village belonged to the ruling People's Alliance Party (PAP). PAP was sure to win the election.

The village's most famous son was Chief the Honourable Marcus Ibe. He was Minister of Culture in the government. Nobody doubted that the Honourable Minister would be re-elected in his constituency. There was no point in opposing him. As the saying goes, it would be like a fly trying to move a dunghill. But a man called Maduka was standing against Marcus. Maduka was a member of the Progressive Organisation Party (POP). He was completely unknown in the village. This made his fight against Marcus even more foolish.

Roof worked for the Honourable Minister during his election campaign. Roof had become a real expert in campaigning. He knew all about elections at village level, regional level or national level. He could always tell the mood of the electorate. For instance, he knew that the ideas of people in Umuofia had changed completely since the last national election. He had warned the Minister about this change months ago.

The price of loyalty

Five years had passed since the last election. In that time the villagers learned a lot about politics. They saw that politicians became very wealthy. They were given honours: they were made chiefs and doctors. (The people did not understand what an 'honorary doctor' was: in their simple way, they thought that a doctor should be able to heal the sick.) Anyhow, these honours came very easily to the Minister.

Only the other day, the villagers argued, Marcus Ibe was just a mission school teacher. He was not successful. In fact, he was going to be fired, because one of the female teachers at the school was pregnant. Then politics came to their village. Wisely, Marcus joined the PAP. That saved his job.

Today, Marcus was Chief the Honourable. He had two long cars. He had just built himself the biggest house anyone had seen in these parts. There was no running water or electricity in Umuofia. But Marcus had his own machine to supply electricity to his new house.

But let it be said that none of these successes had
gone to Marcus's head. He was still devoted to
his people. Whenever he could, he left the good
things of the capital and came back to his village.

Marcus knew where his good luck came from.
He was not like the little bird Nza. One day Nza
ate and drank too much. Then he went out and
challenged his personal spirit to a fight. Of
course, Nza was destroyed. Marcus was not like
that. He called his new house 'Umuofia
Mansions', in honour of his village. The house

was opened by the Archbishop. On that day
Marcus slaughtered five bulls and many goats
for the people.

Everyone was full of praise for Marcus. One old
man said: 'Our son is a good man. He is not like
the mortar, which turns its back on the ground

as soon as food comes its way. We voted for him. He will not turn his back on us now.'

But when the feasting was over, the villagers thought about how rich Marcus had become. They told themselves that in the last election they did not understand the power of the ballot paper. Five years ago, they gave Marcus their votes free of charge. But now they thought they should be paid a little for voting.

Thanks to Roof's warning, Chief the Honourable Marcus Ibe was prepared for this new way of thinking. Before the election he drew five months' salary in advance. He changed a few hundred pounds into shining shillings. Then he armed his campaign boys with little bags full of shillings.

In the day, Marcus made his speeches.

At night his faithful helpers went around whispering and handing out shillings. Roof was the most trusted of these campaigners.

Bargaining with the elders

One night Roof met a group of elders in the house of Ogbuefi Ezenwa. Ezenwa was an honoured traditional leader.

'Minister Marcus comes from our village,' Roof said to the elders. 'He is one of our own sons. What greater honour can a village have? And do you know why we have been singled out for this honour? I will tell you: it is because the leaders of PAP do more for us than for other people. Whether or not we cast our paper for Marcus, PAP will continue to rule. Think of the running water they have promised us ...'

Besides Roof and his assistant there were five elders present. The room was lit by an old hurricane lamp with a cracked, sooty, glass chimney. It gave out a yellowish light. The elders sat on very low stools. On the floor, right in front of each of them, lay two shilling pieces.

Outside, beyond the locked door, the moon kept a straight face.

'We believe every word you say,' said Ezenwa. 'Every one of us will drop his paper for Marcus. Who would leave an *ozo* feast and go to a poor ritual meal? Tell Marcus he has our papers. And our wives' votes too. But what we do say is that two shillings is shameful.'

Ezenwa brought the lamp close to the money before him. It looked as if he was making sure he had not mistaken the value of the coins.

'Yes, two shillings is too shameful,' Ezenwa went on. 'If Marcus were a poor man I would understand. Then I would be the first to give him my vote free, as I did before. But today Marcus is a great man and does his things like a great man. We did not ask him for money yesterday. We shall not ask him tomorrow. But today is our day. We have climbed the *iroko* tree today. We would be foolish not to take down all the firewood we need.'

Roof had to agree. Lately he had been taking down a lot of firewood himself. Only yesterday he had asked Marcus for one of his many rich robes. And Marcus gave it to him! Last Sunday Roof had been drinking beer from Marcus's refrigerator. When he pulled out his fifth bottle, Marcus's wife told him to stop. But Marcus rebuked her in front of everyone. (This wife, by the way, was the same teacher who nearly got Marcus into trouble.)

But the best story was this one: Recently, Roof and another villager had argued over some land. There was a court case to decide who the real owner was. Roof got Marcus's driver to take

him to the site in Marcus's long car. The judge
was so impressed that Roof won the case.

So Roof understood the elders about the
firewood. When good luck comes your way,
you should make the most of it.

'All right,' Roof said in English, and then went
back to Ibo. 'Let us not fight about small things.'

He stood up, straightened his robes and plunged
his hand once more into the bag. Then he bent
down and gave one shilling more to every man.
He did not put the coins into their hands,
but on the floor in front of them.

The men did not even touch the things. They just looked at the floor and shook their heads. Roof got up again and gave each man one more shilling.

'I am through,' Roof said defiantly. 'Go cast your paper for the enemy if you like!'

The elders knew that he didn't really mean it. They also knew how far to go without becoming undignified. They each made a speech to calm Roof down. By the time the last man had spoken, they were able to pick up the coins from the floor without losing their dignity ...

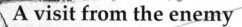

A visit from the enemy

The 'enemy' Roof had spoken
about was the Progressive
Organisation Party (POP).

This party had been formed by the tribes who lived down the coast. The party promised to save its members from 'total political, cultural, social and religious destruction'.

POP had no chance of winning an election in this part of the country. Even so, they decided to stand against PAP. The POP candidate was called Maduka. POP gave cars and loudspeakers to a few local troublemakers and thugs. These men went around making a lot of noise. No one knew exactly how much money POP was spending in Umuofia. But it was said to be a lot. POP's campaigners would end up very rich, no doubt.

Roof thought everything was 'moving according to plan'. But then one night he received a strange visit. The leader of the POP campaign team and another man came to see him. The leader and Roof knew each other well. They might even be called friends. But the visit was cold and businesslike. No words were wasted. The man placed five pounds on the floor before Roof. He said, 'We want your vote.'

Roof got up from his chair. He went to the
outside door and closed it carefully. Then he
returned to his chair. While he was doing this he
had time to think about the offer. As he spoke
his eyes never left the red notes on the floor. He
seemed to be mesmerised by the picture on the
notes. It showed a cocoa farmer harvesting his
crops.

'You know I work for Marcus,' Roof said weakly. 'It will be very bad ...'

'Marcus will not be there when you put your paper in the box,' the man said. 'We have plenty of work to do tonight. Are you taking this or not?'

'It will not be heard outside this room?' asked Roof.

'We want votes, not gossip.'

'All right,' said Roof in English.

The man nudged his helper. The helper brought forward something covered with a red cloth. He removed the cover. It was an *iyi*.

This frightening magic charm was kept in a clay pot. There were feathers sticking out of it.

'The *iyi* comes from Mbanta. You know what that means. Swear that you will vote for Maduka. If you fail to do so, this *iyi* take note.'

Roof's heart nearly flew out of his body when he saw the *iyi*. He knew the fame of Mbanta in these things.

But Roof was a man who made up his mind quickly. He would have a single vote and he would vote in secret. What difference could one vote make? What could it take away from Marcus's certain victory? Nothing.

'I will cast my paper for Maduka,' Roof said. 'If not, this *iyi* take note.'

'Das all,' said the man as he rose. His helper covered up the pot again and took it back to their car.

'You know Maduka has no chance against Marcus,' Roof said at the door.

'It is enough that he gets a few votes now,' the man replied. 'Next time he will get more. People will hear that he gives out pounds, not shillings. Then they will listen.'

Election day

Election morning. Every five years the great day
comes when the people use their power. There
were posters on the walls of houses, tree trunks
and telegraph poles. Most of the posters had
been torn by wind and rain. But the few that

were still in one piece called out their message to those who could read. Vote for the People's Alliance Party! Vote for the Progressive Organisation Party! Vote for PAP! Vote for POP! The torn posters called out as much of the message as they could.

As usual, Chief the Honourable Marcus Ibe was doing things in grand style. He had hired a highlife band from Umuru. It was against the law to have bands at the voting booths. So Marcus put the band at a safe distance. Many villagers danced to the music, holding their ballot papers up in the air, before going on to the booths.

Chief the Honourable Marcus Ibe sat in the 'owner's corner' of his huge green car. He smiled and nodded. One enlightened villager came up to the car. He shook hands with the great man and said in advance, 'Congrats!' Hundreds of people tried to copy this villager. They shook Marcus's hand and said, 'Corngrass!'

Roof and the other organisers marched up and down. They gave last minute advice to the voters and poured with sweat.

A group of illiterate women arrived. They seemed ready to burst with excitement.

'Do not forget,' Roof said to them, 'our sign is the motor car ...'

'Like the one Marcus is sitting inside,' said an old woman.

'Thank you, mother,' said Roof. 'It is the same car. The box with the car on it is the box for you. Don't look at the other box, with the man's head. It is for those whose heads are not correct.'

This was greeted with loud laughter. Roof

glanced at the Minister. His glance said, 'Look how busy I am.' The Minister gave him a smile of thanks.

'Vote for the car!' Roof shouted so loud that all the veins in his neck stood out. 'Vote for the car and you will ride in it!'

'Or if we don't, our children will,' piped the same clever old woman.

The band struck up a new number: 'Why walk when you can ride ...'

Time to choose

Chief the Honourable Marcus looked calm and confident. But he always worried about every little detail. He knew he would win. The newspapers would call it a 'landslide victory'. But even so, he did not want to throw away a single vote. As soon as the first rush of voters was over, he wanted his campaign boys to vote. He asked them to go one at a time and put in their ballot papers.

'Roof, you had better go first,' Marcus said.

Roof began to feel unhappy. But he let no one
see it. All morning he had been deeply worried.
But he hid his worry by keeping very busy.
Now he rushed off in his springy way towards
the booths.

A policeman at the entrance searched Roof for
illegal ballot papers and let him pass. Then the
electoral officer explained to him about the two
boxes. There was one for Marcus and one for
Maduka. Marcus's box had a picture of a car on

it. Maduka's box had a man's head. Roof had to put his ballot paper into one of the two boxes. By this time the spring had gone right out of his walk.

Roof sidled into the booth. He was confronted by the car and the head. He brought out his ballot paper from his pocket and looked at it. How could he betray Marcus, even in secret? He decided to go back to POP's campaign leader and return his five pounds ... Five pounds! He knew at once it was impossible. He had sworn on that *iyi*. The notes were red; the cocoa farmer was busy working.

Just then Roof heard a quiet voice. The policeman was asking the electoral officer why Roof was taking so long in the booth. 'Abi na pickin im de born?' the policeman asked.

Quick as lightning a thought leapt into Roof's mind. He folded the paper in half. Then he tore it in two along the crease and put one half in each box. He was careful to put the first half in Maduka's box. And he also said out loud: 'I vote for Maduka.'

They marked his thumb with purple ink which could not be washed off. This was so that he would not be able to come back and vote again. He left the booth looking as happy and confident as ever.

Your Vote: more than just a mark!

This election took place in Nigeria, but there are things we can learn here in South Africa. Here are Roof and Sibongile to tell you about it.

'I am Roof from Umuofia, Nigeria. As you know I am a campaign worker for PAP in my village. In my country, we had our first free election in 1959. So we have lots of experience with elections.'

'I am Sibongile. I live in Hammerskraal, South Africa. We had our first democratic election in 1994. I still remember how exciting it was! I couldn't believe it when I finally put my ballot in the box. This year, I decided to be a campaign worker for my party. Since I started, I have learnt a lot.

For example, I have learnt what an election campaign is. Election campaigns happen close to election time. Every political party wants you to vote for them. So there is competition among political parties to win votes. They make promises to people about what they will do if they get into power.

I have been busy going from door to door, telling people about my party. Sometimes people are friendly, and promise to vote for my party, but sometimes they are very rude. Our party has an election manifesto. This is a little booklet which tells what the party stands for and what we *will do if you vote for us.*

I believe that everyone has the right to campaign for the party they like. I wish everyone else felt that way. Sometimes I worry that our election will be ruined by violence. Some people might be afraid to vote. That would be a terrible thing. We worked so hard for the right to vote. The elections must be free and fair.'

So Nigeria has had an earlier experience of democracy in their country than we have. Here are two other differences:

'You read in the story that we vote for one person to represent our region. That person becomes our own Member of Parliament. This is called representation by population, or a constitiuency-based voting system .'

'In South Africa, we have a system called Proportional Representation. This system was agreed upon during negotiations before the 1994 election. In proportional representation people vote for a political party. The party chooses the people who will go to Parliament. The party with the most votes will get the most people in Parliament.'

'Remember in the story, we had two ballot boxes in the voting station. The box for PAP had a picture of a car. The box for POP had a man's head. We were given the ballot papers before we went in. Then we put the ballot papers in the box for the party we wanted.'

'In South Africa, it is different. We do not get our ballot papers until we go into the voting station. Then we put a mark beside the party we want, and put the ballot paper in the box.

In general elections, we vote twice: first for the National Assembly, which is the government for all of South Africa. We also vote for the government for

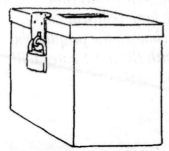

the province we live in. The two ballots are different colours, but we put them in the same box.'

'But, like Nigeria, we have a secret ballot. Only you know who you vote for.

That reminds me, Roof. When you were at the voting station you tore your ballot paper into two pieces, didn't you? I know you were scared because you had sworn on the **iyi** but do you think your vote counted?'

'Hey, you are right. I don't think my vote counted because I tore my ballot paper. How would they know who I was voting for? I guess I spoilt my ballot paper. No one got my vote.'

'Don't you think that **iyi** business is silly?'

'No! The **iyi** is very important in our culture. I was raised to believe that it is very powerful.'

'Sorry. I didn't mean to insult you. We also have important beliefs in our culture.'

How elections work in South Africa

Every five years, the citizens of South Africa have the right to vote in national and provincial, or regional elections. We vote in local elections every four years, for the people who take care of our cities, towns and villages.

Proportional Representation System

There are two kinds of election systems used in the world: Nigeria uses the constituency-based system. Remember Chief the Honourable Marcus Ibe in our story? He was the candidate the people of Umuofia elected to represent their village in Parliament. We say that Umuofia was his constituency. Usually in this kind of system, you vote for a person.

The South African system is different. Here we vote for a political party. Our system is called Proportional Representation. This is how it works:

Each party sends a number of people to Parliament. The number of people each party sends will depend on the number of votes that party gets.

There are 400 people in the Parliament in South Africa. If one party gets half of the votes, then that party will be able to send 200 people to Parliament – that is half of 400. Another party might get a quarter of the votes, so it will send a quarter of 400, or 100 people.

The party that gets the most votes and gets the most people in Parliament is called the governing or

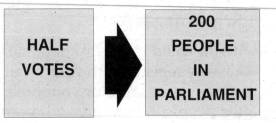

majority group. Their leader will become the president of South Africa.

Before the elections each party prepares a list of candidates. When the voting is over, the party candidates are given seats in Parliament. People who are at the top of the list are the first to go to Parliament. For example, if a party wins fifty seats, then the first fifty people on the list will go to Parliament. These people are called Members of parliament, or MPs.

'Does that mean that you do not know the MP's you elect? Who do you go to if you have a problem?'

'After the elections, each MP is given an area in the country to take care of, and money to set up a constituency

office. So it's true we might not know the MP in our area, but we can contact the office for help. If the MP does not help us, we have the right to complain to the political party.'

Registering to Vote

If you voted in the last national election, you have already registered to vote. That means your name is on the voter's roll for your area. This is a list of all the people in your area who can vote. If your name is not on the list, you cannot vote.

A few months before the next election, you will have a chance to register to vote. This is what you must do:

1. First, you must have an ID card with a bar-code on it.

2. Take your ID to the registration point near the place where you live. You can find out where this is in newspapers, on the radio or TV before the election. OR your can ask at your municipal offices.

3. Fill in the voter registration form. You can get help with this if you need it.

4. The officer will point a Zip-Zip machine at your ID book. It will scan the bar code, and the computer will put your name on the voters' roll.

5. The registering official will stick a receipt in your ID book. It gives the date, time and number of the station where you registered.

If you are already on the voters' roll, you don't have to register again, unless you move to a new area.

Who can vote?

You can vote if you are:

✗ a South African citizen
✗ 18 years old on or before the election
✗ registered to vote in your area
✗ voting in the same area where you registered
✗ in South Africa on election day.

'My cousin and her husband are permanent residents in South Africa. Can they vote?'

'No, they must become citizens if they want to vote.'

Voting

'I am nervous about voting, because I have never done it before. I am afraid some people will force me to vote for a party I don't want.'

'Don't worry. Voting is easy, once you know what to do. There are two important things to remember:

1. *Your vote is secret. When you vote, you will go behind a screen, and no one else will see how you vote.*

2. *Make sure you know who you will vote for before you go into the voting station. On the ballot paper, you will see:*

    — *The name of the party*

    — *The symbol, or logo for the party, and*

    — *A picture of the party's leader.*

You will put a mark beside the name of your party.'

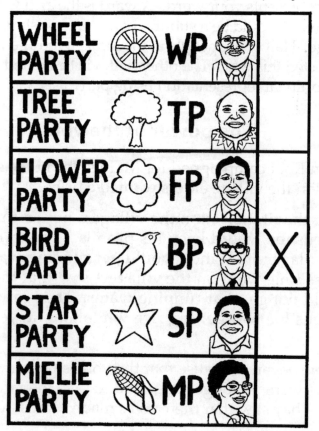

Local Elections

Local elections are a little different from national and provincial elections. For example, you must register separately for local elections. You can register near your home, or near your workplace if you work far from home. But remember, you must vote in the area where you have registered.

In local elections you vote for a person called a councillor, who represents your ward. A ward is the area where you live. It could be a suburb, part of a township, or a village. Half of the people in the local government will be elected this way. The other half will be elected by proportional representation using party lists.

The power of the vote

When Roof campaigned for Marcus Ibe in the second election the village elders wanted a bribe.

After the first election the villagers hoped that Marcus Ibe would keep his promises. He promised the villagers that they would get running water. But as time went on the villagers saw that they would not get that running water. They saw that Marcus Ibe was getting rich while they stayed poor.

People began to realise that the vote is power. The elders were no longer prepared to give their vote for free. They saw that their votes made Marcus Ibe rich.

They also wanted to benefit. They wanted to be paid for their votes.

Why did the elders choose to be bribed? They could have refused to vote for Marcus again because he did not keep his promises. Why didn't they? We do not know for sure.

But we do know that the people of Umuofia only knew one party, the People's Alliance Party (PAP), to which they all belonged. So there was no real opposition. The villagers could not see a way to use their vote to make changes. Even though there was the Progressive Organisation Party (POP), it was not well-known in their village.

Multi-party democracy

In South Africa, there will be several different parties asking for our vote. Of course these parties have different policies and beliefs. This is called a multi-party democracy. It gives people many choices. If a party does not keep its promises, people can vote it out of power and put another party in its place. In a multi-party democracy political parties compete against each other for power. They want to have the best leaders and programmes so that people will vote for them.

[On this page are the logos of parties which have participated in South African elections before.]

Bribery

Bribery means buying a favour. In most countries this is illegal. In South Africa, we have an Electoral Act. This is a set of rules for the election. The Electoral Act says that it is illegal to offer money for votes, or to take money for votes. People who do it are breaking the law. Bribes can come in many forms. Political parties can bribe you by giving you gifts or giving parties with free food and drink.

You know, you can take a gift from someone, especially if you are afraid to say no to them. But, remember your vote is secret. So just be sure that you don't swear on the *iyi* when you take the gift!

Women and the vote

'I liked the story about the election in Nigeria. But on page 11, the elders promised Roof that their wives would vote for PAP. This made me angry. How can they make promises like that? "One person – one vote" means no one can tell you how to vote: not your husband, not your wife, not your boss. No one.'

What do women want?

The government has made many changes since 1994.
But there are still many problems, especially for
women. Here is what some women say:

'I want better
health care for
people with
HIV and
AIDS.'

'I want the right
to own my own
land.'

'I want
better
education,
for me and
my
children.'

'I want violence
against women
and children to
stop.'

'Did you know that one third of the MP's in South Africa are
women? And many women hold senior posts, like ministers.
This is great, but I would like to see even more women in
parliament. Who knows better what we need than a woman?
You can push to make sure women get into
parliament by checking your party's list before the
election. Tell your party you want half of the people
on its list to be women.'

Election promises

The Umuofia villagers voted in the first election with the hope that they would get a better life. But all they saw was Marcus Ibe getting two long cars, building himself the biggest house and getting electricity for himself. Before the election Marcus Ibe promised people running water.

But he did not keep his promise.

This is a common thing and it happens in many countries. Throughout Africa, politicians have failed to keep promises made during the liberation struggle. There are reasons why this happens.

Not enough money for everything

Most poor and jobless people have suffered for a long time. They expect the government to bring quick changes to their lives. But changes cost money. The government does not have enough money to pay for all the changes at once. It is forced to make some changes first and leave others.

Battling forces

The poor people hope their lives will get better quickly, but the rich do not want to lose what they have. The government would like to please everyone. It can't. So it listens to the loudest voices.

Usually, these are the voices of rich and powerful people.

For example, Roof won his court case because Marcus Ibe's chauffeur drove him to court. The judge saw that he was powerful.

Self-interest

Sometimes, politicians can use politics to get rich. Remember Marcus Ibe in the story? He was just a simple teacher before he got elected to represent his village. When he got elected he developed a taste for comfort and luxury. He built himself the biggest house in the village with electricity and running water. He forgot about the people who chose him. Some leaders who come from the oppressed and exploited also change after liberation. They use politics to get rich quickly.

What will happen in South Africa?

'I remember how we struggled before our first elections. Our slogans were "Votes for All", "Jobs for All", "Free and Compulsory Education for All", and so on. Now all South Africans can vote, but most of us are still struggling for a better life.

Each time there is an election, we hear political parties promising to make things better. But do they keep their promises? What happens if they cannot? We are not rich or powerful. How can we make sure the government will listen to us? ...'

Ways to make your voice heard

We know how important it is to vote. The vote gives you a voice in the running of the country. You can change things by using the vote and can make things happen with the vote. But this is not enough. Between each election, you must also make your voice heard. It is better to do this in a strong, well-organised group.

48

Here are some examples.

TRADE UNIONS

WOMEN

NO LAND NO VOTE!

TAXI OWNERS

RURAL COMMUNITIES

'There are three things I have learned from your story.

One is that a vote is not something that should be paid for.
We should vote for the party that we believe in, and that
will work hard for the people.

Second, if we are not happy with what the government
does, we must tell them. We can speak alone, or we can
organise and speak as a group. We must let the
government know that if they do not keep their promises,
we, the voters can fire them!

But most important, every vote counts, and everyone's
vote is equal. If we want change in our country, we must
all get out there and vote. And we have the right to decide
for ourselves who to vote for. No one can stop us now.'

Word list

Abi na pickin im de born (page 27) – Is he giving birth to a baby? In other words, why is he taking such a long time

ballot paper (pages 7, 22, 24, 25, 26) – piece of paper used in voting

betray (page 26) – harm; be disloyal to

businesslike (page 16) – efficient

campaign (pages 2, 3, 7, 16, 24, 26) – actions planned to win the support of voters, by holding meetings, putting up posters, etc.

campaigners (pages 9, 16) – people who work for a politician during an election campaign

candidate (page 16) – person standing for election

charm (page 18) – a thing with magical powers

citizen (pages 34, 37) - a person who has the right to live, work and vote in a country, and who carries the passport of that country.

congrats (page 22) – short way of saying 'congratulations'; some of the villagers cannot say 'congrats' properly, and so they say 'corngrass'

constituency (page 2) – town or area represented by a politician

culture (page 2) – the arts, like music or drama

defiantly (page 14) – in a challenging way

devoted to (page 5) – very loyal to

dignity (page 14) – sense of self-importance

dunghill (page 2) – heap of animal droppings

elders (pages 9, 13, 14) – old leaders

election (pages 2, 3, 4, 7, 16, 20) – where people can

vote to choose political leaders

electoral officer (pages 25, 27) – person in charge of voting

electorate (page 3) – all the people who have the right to vote

expert (page 3) – someone who knows a lot about a subject

faithful (page 9) – loyal

guide (page 2) – show the way to

harvesting (page 17) – gathering

highlife band (page 22) – West African name for a band that plays popular dance music

honorary doctor (page 4) – someone given a university degree as a special honour or mark of respect

honourable (pages 1, 2, 4, 7 ...) – highly respected

honours (page 4) – awards

illiterate (page 22) – unable to read or write

impressed (page 13) – filled with admiration

in secret (pages 19, 26) – without anyone else knowing

iroko (page 12) – the *iroko* tree is the biggest tree in the forest and so people do not often climb it

landslide victory (page 24) – an election won by a large number of votes

mesmerised (page 17) – completely fascinated

mortar (page 6) – a heavy bowl in which food is ground up with a pestle; in South Africa sometimes called a 'stampblock'

municipal offices (pages 16, 30, 31 ...) – the place where the municipal government, or

local government, does its work.
'Municipal' means city, town or village.

nudged (page 18) – pushed gently

opposing (page 2) – fighting against

ozo (page 11) – a high title or name of respect; when a man is awarded this title he gives a big feast for the people of his village

political party (page 36) – a group of people who come together because they have the same beliefs about politics and about how to run their country. They register their party, choose a leader, then fight to win the election. Examples: ANC, DP, PAC.

politicians (page 4) – people who take part in government

pounds and shillings (pages 7, 9, 11 ...) – money used in Britain and some other countries

praise (page 6) – things said in admiration

rebuked (page 12) – scolded

re-elected (page 2) – voted into power again

ritual (pages 11) – ceremonial; rituals are special acts or ceremonies that people perform as part of their traditions, for example, church services

robes (pages 12, 13) – long, loose kind of clothing

springy (pages 25, 26) – bouncy

strange (page 16) – unusual

trusted (page 9) – reliable

undignified (page 14) – foolish and embarrassing

voting booths (page 22) – small enclosed places in which people vote